I dedicate this book to my mom, Theresa B. Robinson. Without her instructions and guidance I would never have completed this assignment. My love for you is eternal, mom! Thank you for instilling determination and fearlessness within me.

To my friends Gabi Bucataru and Robert Murphy, thank you for your time, creativity, and zealousness regarding this literary work. Together, we proved that people from different backgrounds and cultures can create something meaningful and beautiful... Especially when the purpose is for the greater good of humanity.

As a five year old
I ran from hate,
Ran to be safe,
From those who would Intimidate,
Invalidate,
And lie in wait,

Mother would educate
Of those who chose
To segregate,
Denigrate,
Desecrate,
Devastate,

I would await
A change of state,
A day to liberate,
To celebrate,
And graduate,
One day to
Elevate

Far beyond the hate.

My name is Lizzie, and I was born October 25, 1938, in the small town of Archer, Florida. My family and I lived on my daddy's farm. It was huge! There were nearly 300 acres of land filled with crops and livestock. I always felt safe and loved at home. The color of my skin didn't provoke ugly words and stares from white people on our farm. So, whenever I left the farm, I ran.

Right now, you're invited to come on a run or walk down memory lane.

"I was about five years old when the real life lessons began ..."

The story of my life is told in every step. My feet carried me down the road, often too tired to go further. I felt that I was often running from the darkness of others, sometimes running to the light.

As a child, I walked a total of 6 miles to school every day, 3 miles there and 3 miles returning home. My feet are calloused, bruised, and achy, but the story they tell is triumphant and true.

Come with me, as we imaginatively travel back in time to an era where most people didn't have phones, televisions, cars, running water, or plumbing to use the bathroom. As a young girl, I remember pumping water from the well for bathing, cooking, and drinking. I never had a hot shower as a child.

Guess what? Having shoes to wear was a luxury, whether they were hand-me-downs or brand new (extremely rare). I was the youngest of my siblings, and my older brothers and sister didn't have shoes either. We were poor and this is how life was back then.

I am a descendant of the esteemed Rosewood family, and this is our story.

Rosewood was a small, peaceful town with beautiful people. Unfortunately, it no longer exists. However, I still walk and run sometimes through Rosewood to tell my story. Surprisingly, not even the railroad tracks remain. There is only one old home that still stands.

When I first began attending school in Archer, most days I walked to school. Sometimes, my older cousin would hoist me on his back and carry me to and from school. Yes, he carried me the whole 6 miles. He was kind and patient, and he never said carrying me was a burden. Our family was like that!

We shared everything with each other, and we did it without any hesitation.

What belonged to one family, belonged to everyone.
Sharing and caring for each other was as natural as
breathing.

We were taught to work hard on our farm. We fed the chickens, milked the cattle, and we planted and harvested crops daily. There was always work to do and I felt good when I did my part.

My story is an account of my race. My mother always told me to run when white folks were nearby. Whenever we saw trucks or cars approaching us, we ran and hid in the woods to avoid racist people.

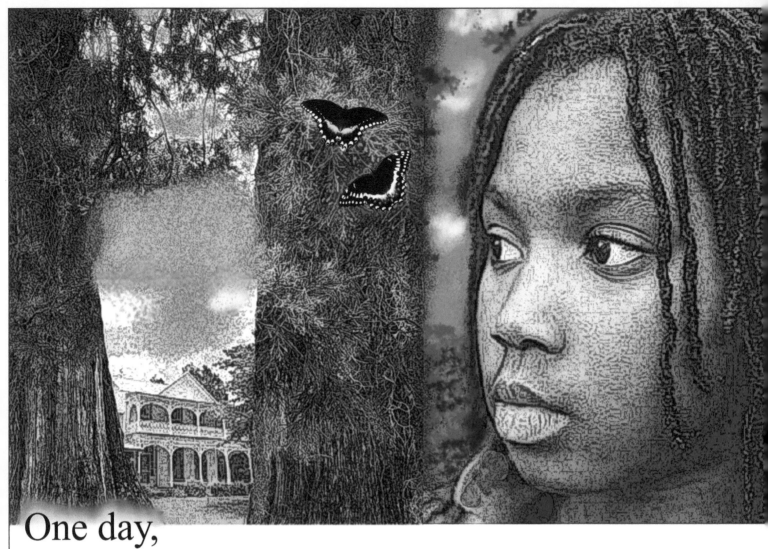

One day,

my mom told me the story of my auntie, the Rosewood schoolteacher. I learned that my family lived in a quiet community that was thriving until one day their lives were taken and their homes were burned to the ground. She told me to never forget what happened and to ensure the truth would never be lost. My mind didn't understand how people could hate and hurt one another so terribly. So, I promise to keep speaking the truth about the people of Rosewood for as long as I live.

I made a promise to my family.
I made a promise to myself. For
as long as these feet keep moving,
I will continue to keep those promises.

As a little girl, I often wondered why the white men drove down the dirt roads and said such mean and hateful things! Most times, I was so scared. Why did they hate us so much? These questions are never really answered, and it bothered me. I started to hate them for how they treated us. We didn't do anything wrong; the color of our skin made them hate us.

One day when I was walking home from school, I saw a beautiful black butterfly. It was unlike any butterfly I had seen before. Then something quite strange happened. The butterfly seemed to read my thoughts.

I'd never seen a black butterfly, and the closer it got to me, it was as if it spoke to me saying, "You and I are so much alike." We're both dark, fair, graceful, and lovely. Beneath our wings, we have loving hearts, that are full of kindness and goodness. Let's fly together, light the world up, and make it a better place."

The butterfly seemed to be saying:

'Just like all living things need water,
all living things need love and kindness.
Sometimes humans have a hard time learning that.'

From that day forward, I often saw my new friend the butterfly as I walked to and from school.

I learned many valuable lessons
about life as I grew up on our farm.

Love and kindness
comes in many shapes,
sizes, and colors.

Abe wasn't black.
He wasn't white.
He was both.
And he was all the more beautiful because of the
wonderful painted patterns on his body.
He taught me that colors could blend nicely alone or
together. He seemed to know what some humans
didn't know.

Most everywhere
I looked there seemed
to be something in
nature with a lesson for me.

Butterflies have hard days too, Lizzie. Strong winds, rain, birds and other insects sometimes bring us harm. It may not seem fair and sometimes it can make us sad. But beyond those sad days, there are many good days filled with sunshine and positive moments.
You have a beautiful smile and a wonderful heart.
No one or nothing will ever change that. Whenever you're having a hard day, remember this day. And so will I.

'Life is never easy and often seems unfair. Find the good in yourself and in others even when its hard. It will surprise you what changes you'll see in yourself and others.'

I'll never forget my teachers. They did their best to give us the skills and abilities we needed to prepare for the future. But when my mom told me about my aunt, Mahulda Gussie Brown Carrier, I knew one day I'd follow in her footsteps and become a teacher too. It was my mother's love for her sister, that compelled me to carry on her life's purpose. I knew I could do so much good in the memory of my dear aunt Gussie.

One day in a branch high above me,
I seemed to hear a beautiful voice:

'Birds and butterflies come in many different sizes, shapes, and colors. The song I sing everyday is different from others. My song is special. It's a part of who I am. Your song is special, Lizzie. No one else will ever sing it quite like you!  Find your voice, sing your song loudly and never stop singing!'

I didn't know then that one day
the student would become the
teacher--
A teacher, an educator of minds and hearts.
I would one day tell the story of a beautiful
young teacher of the town of Rosewood, Florida.

There was something magical about the windows and floors of that old school-house. The surface was pitted, and each scuffed marking told stories that had never been heard. The walls and windows were silent witnesses to the good and the bad. My feet felt the imperfections in the floors, but I sensed the determination of those who had stood there before me.

I loved the big windows because they allowed the afternoon sunlight to come through. Sometimes, I'd close my eyes and imagine my feet like those of a ballerina, dancing and drifting across the floor.

That old schoolhouse was a special place. It was more than skills of reading, writing and arithmetic. It was a place where dreams, imagination and new discoveries took place.

The pond was always
a place to quietly reflect
about the good things in my
life and the love of my family.

During the summer, the water was the perfect temperature...

When I was 13 years old, my father worked as a sharecropper for a white landowner. My father always told me to lay low inside his truck when the landowner was around. One day, I understood first-hand why my father gave me these instructions.

On this particular day, the white landowner began cursing and shouting ugly words at my daddy. I felt anger raging inside me and couldn't take it any longer. Without thinking, I jumped up and started shouting the same dark, ugly words the man said to my daddy back at him. I know I shocked him. My father wasn't too happy about me defending him. He was usually very quiet and would not respond to the bad behavior. On that day, they both understood I wouldn't allow my dad to be mistreated.

I was enraged! My heart was pounding, my hands were shaking, and I screamed his exact words back at him. My dad was my hero, and he wasn't any of the hateful things the white man called him.

I learned many lessons from my work on the farm. Planting tiny seeds in carefully prepared soil meant that within a matter of months we could enjoy delicious crops of fruits and vegetables. The results were very satisflying, knowing how hard we had worked to get healthy fresh food on our table each day.

Plant a seed,
nurture it with water,
sunshine and rich, dark earth.
And one day, your hard work
results in something quite lovely
and delicious.

I learned another lesson as well, as I got
older. Our thoughts are much like seeds.
Whatever we think about and believe
becomes a part of who we are.

By the light of a kerosene lamp mom worked her magic. She cooked, cleaned and sewed our clothing. We didn't buy most things from a store. Whatever wasn't grown and harvested on the farm we often bartered for. I loved my mother's handiwork and was always amazed by what she could create. I think that went well beyond my childhood. Many decades later she was still sewing and seemed to love what she created as much as we loved wearing the outfits from that wonderful old sewing machine. Sometimes I close my eyes and hear it working away, spinning threads into works of art.

My mom's life was much like her sewing skills. She wove love and kindness into every thread, every stitch, and every fabric of her being. Her example made it possible for us to manage all the trials we faced outside of our community.

From my childhood to well into adult years, my mother's sewing machine worked its' magic. She wove her love into every piece of thread that was spun on that wonderful old machine.

Grandfather Brown was a preacher. Our family read from his well-worn bible each night before supper. I learned to read from it as a young child. I did not understand the power of grandfathers' handwriting until many years later:

forgive four hundred and ninety times

Learning to forgive was a very difficult thing for me. In fact, it took me nearly half a lifetime to understand what it meant and how to apply it in my life.

Just like the seeds in the soil of our farm, forgiveness was planted in my young head and heart.
It began to grow slowly and over many years it created a change in the way I looked at others and the world as a whole. I learned that I needed to let go of bad feelings for others who may have hurt me in some way.

Life on the farm was never easy,
but working and playing together was
a great learning experience for all of us.

One day, the black butterfly taught me another important lesson.

People change just like butterflies. Sometimes they change for the good and other times for the bad. However, real change occurs on the inside and this is what matters! What is on the inside of you, light or darkness? I encourage you to be the light!

On another day I encountered a beautiful baby bird that said:

I know I seem a bit helpless right now, but I was born to fly! My wings aren't quite developed yet, but each day I get closer to flying. Lizzie, you and I are more alike than we seem and one day you will fly too! In the meantime, you keep running as fast as you can.

Being a teacher was an exciting chapter in my life! I made this promise to myself, my mama and auntie. I taught more than reading, writing, and arithmetic. I influenced children's lives in the most unimaginable ways, and they did the same for me.

Before I started teaching, it was hard sometimes to see the light in white people. One day, one of my students, an adorable innocent little white girl, took my hand and led me out of darkness. I felt a new day emerging. Decades of hurt and anger melted away. This little girl was an angel sent from above. She taught me that forgiveness was possible!

From that day forward, whenever she reached her little white hand out for my brown hand, a beautiful flower seemed to bloom. Her sincerity was pure, simple, and powerful.

A wise man once said,
"A true friend is someone
who reaches for your hand
and touches your heart."

The little girl, who once ran with calloused feet to school, and through fields and dirt roads is much older now. However, I'm still running and telling the story of Rosewood.

When I close my eyes at night, sometimes I hear the sound of a distant train whistle. I also hear my mother's words when she first told me to run and why I must never stop. Although the Rosewood massacre happened more than 100 years ago, the story of my people is still relevant and needs to be told. My purpose is to ensure no one ever forgets!

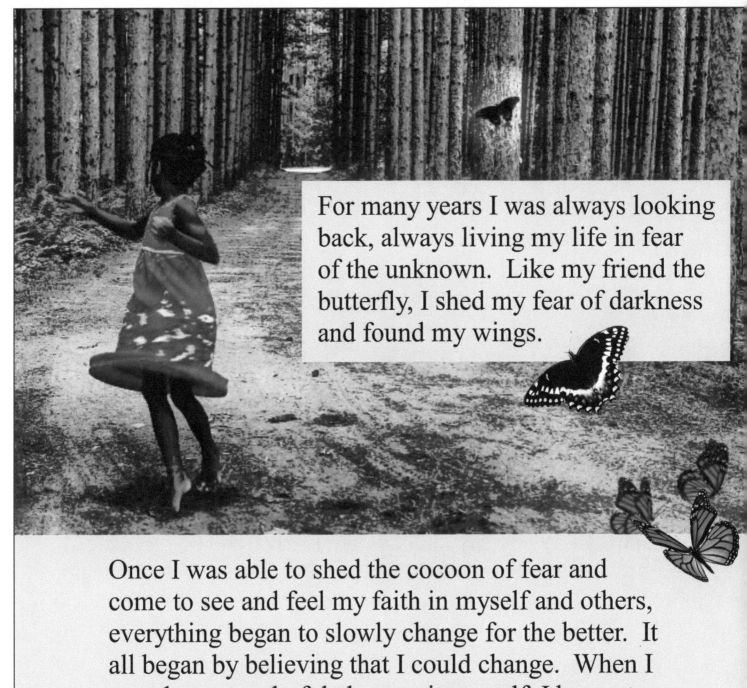

For many years I was always looking back, always living my life in fear of the unknown. Like my friend the butterfly, I shed my fear of darkness and found my wings.

Once I was able to shed the cocoon of fear and come to see and feel my faith in myself and others, everything began to slowly change for the better. It all began by believing that I could change. When I saw those wonderful changes in myself, I began to see good things in others--even in those who I had feared in the past.

Like a butterfly still in the cocoon
waiting for the perfect moment,
waiting for the the day I could
burst forth and fly away and
find my freedom.
Freedom from fear,
freedom from hate,
freedom from judgement.

I was seeking freedom from the
worries and concerns of what
others might be thinking.
Freedom to run because I was
finally

Free

*Freedom to glow in the
pure light of goodness and joy.*

When we run a race, it's normal to think about a starting point and a finish line. My race has no finish line, it has no end. The human race--black, brown, white, yellow, and all other shades of people and cultures will continue to race for freedom, for equality, for dignity and respect. We are still running and will continue to run. Will you run with me? One day, my feet will wear out and this human heart will stop beating. When that happens, I hope to trade these tired feet for wings. Maybe, just maybe I'll join my friend the butterfly. Maybe I'll be an angel. Whatever awaits me, I'll keep moving and keep singing the song, and telling the story of Rosewood.

Somewhere out there the bells of that beautiful little town are still ringing. Somewhere, children of all colors are running on a school ground as teachers plan and prepare them for lessons of life. I'm still teaching, I'm still running.
I hope you'll join me.

Love,
   Lizzie

Sometimes she walks, sometimes she runs,
She never stops, she's never done,
Her journey is long and never ends,
She's fighting for change, her truth transcends;

The scripts of men whose actions repress,
She breaks the bonds, her truth expressed,
From sister souls, long since gone,
She carries light for those yet to come,

She falls at times in anguished strain,
The journey fraught with sorrow and pain,
But in dark times of doubt and grief,
From heavens' clarion she finds relief,

And presses on through blood and tears,
Her urgent cause, transcending fears,
Undeterred, she runs the race,
Head held high with noble grace.

Her mission clear, she journeys on,
Bursting forth, hands clasps baton,
To generations yet unborn,
Feet press forward, in spite of thorns,

Renewed of courage and seasoned wisdom,
To legions of sisters, her shared vision,
So they, like her can run the race,
Higher powers define her place,

Sometimes she walks, sometimes she runs,
She'll never stop, she's just begun!
As cheering crowds become distant voices,
In silent reverie her soul rejoices;

Her goal in sight, she runs towards,
The race itself her great reward.

It is my fate
to
Create,
A time to
Celebrate,
Commemorate,
Truth,

To
Advocate,
Consecrate,
Dedicate,
Venerate,
And
Perpetuate
Rosewood

Lizzie Robinson Jenkins has encompassed several roles throughout her lifetime... She is an educator, activist and prominent advocate for social justice and equality. As the founder of The Real Rosewood Foundation, she has dedicated her life to ensuring that the true legacy of Rosewood is never forgotten.

For more information and opportunities to connect with The Real Rosewood Foundation, please visit:
 http://www.rosewoodflorida.com

Remember Rosewood

All that remains are the keepers of the story,
In hallowed ground, just beyond the glory,
Innocents suffered ravages of hate,
Their voices cry out, 'Remember our fate!'
A culture of silence, fear and shame,
Legacy of hope now calls out their names,
Remember Rosewood, the peaceful place,
Remember the people of dignity and grace,
Mankinds' darkness a distant memory,
To perished innocents a sacred reverie,
Sentiments of sadness and grief live still,
Keepers of the promise must fulfill,
Trees whisper on winds of sorrow,
Pleading for change on new tomorrows,
Crimson wood holds their story,
Roots run deep in earthly glory,
Nigh a century gone with time,
Echoes still the church bell's chime.

rob murphy -- august 2020

CPSIA information can be obtained
at www.ICGtesting.com
Printed in the USA
JSHW070613190123
36281JS00002B/2